SOULFUL HOLIDAYS

Written by: Ciara L. Hill

Soulful Holidays

Published by:
Lawton Classic Books
Bowie, Maryland 20716

Illustrated by: Christian Krabbe

Printed in the United States of America

ISBN: 978-1-7341565-4-6 (Paperback)
ISBN: 978-1-7341565-5-3 (Hardcover)
ISBN: 978-1-7341565-6-0 (Electronic Book)

Library of Congress Control Number: 2021915389

www.ciaralhillbooks.com

This Book Belongs To

_____

I dedicate this book to my family
for all the fond memories we have created
and for new memories yet to come.
And to everyone who makes
the holiday season soulful and magical.

The holidays are happy times that come around each year.
A chance for celebration with your friends and family near.

We mark the Yuletide season in a lot of different ways.
And African-Americans celebrate soulful holidays.

The kitchen table's covered with the things you love to eat.
Delicious smells of cooking fill the air on every street.

Fried chicken, cornbread, collard greens, and creamy mac 'n cheese,
peach cobbler, sweet potato pie, a bowl of black-eyed peas.

There's every kind of sweet and treat and dishes you adore.
And plenty there for everyone. You couldn't ask for more.

Outside, the kids make angels in the snow upon the ground.

Then run back to their cozy homes to nestle safe and sound.

The grown-ups play a card game, such as Uno, Gin, or Spades,
to noisy peals of laughter as the children play charades.

There's grandpa telling stories of the way it used to be,
while everyone sits and listens around the Christmas tree.

Then Silent Night is playing; the Temptations famous song.
And everybody knows the words and tries to sing along.

You're looking out for Santa Claus
and hope he's on his way,
with all his trusty reindeer who must
pull his heavy sleigh.

With tons and tons of presents to
deliver round the world,
his job is spreading happiness to all
the boys and girls.

Each child has made a careful list
and also checked it twice,
and hopes that Santa got the word
they've all been very nice.

You leave a plate of cookies and
some milk for him to sip,
as you figure, he might need a snack
on such a lengthy trip.

And you're longing for the morning
just to see what Santa brings.
So you go to bed without a fuss
to dream of wondrous things.

You wake before the sunrise
and go rushing down the stairs.
It's really way too early,
but the adults do not care.

They understand that children are excited for the day.
And play the tune, This Christmas, sung by Donny Hathaway.

There's wrapping paper everywhere as ribbons are untied.
And lots of joyful dapping when you find out what's inside.

'Tis the season to be jolly and wish everybody well,
and the time we get together to recall the First Noel.

13

But though Christmas is a lot of fun, you have to understand there are other great traditions taking place across the land.

For example, there is Kwanzaa, and it lasts for seven days, when the heritage of Africa is proudly on display.

It's when African-Americans can celebrate their past, and their present, and the future of a culture built to last.

The kinara on the table at the center of the scene
holds a row of special candles colored red and black, and green

All the candles have a meaning, and you light one every night.
And it must be done in order, so you have to get it right.

There are seven different principles to follow as a guide
that can help you be a person full of purpose, love, and pride.

You celebrate togetherness, a bond that never ends,
a community of people made of family and of friends.

And of course, throughout the holiday there's also lots of fun,
from the very early morning till the Kwanzaa day is done.

There are people wearing clothing that is African attire,
such as kaftans or dashikis, or whatever they desire.

There are paper decorations and a bright mkeka mat
for the middle of the table where some ears of corn are sat.

There is feasting, there is dancing to the beat of djembe
drums. And the giving of zawadi, which are gifts for everyone.

18

Does your family honor Kwanzaa?
Maybe Christmas is your thing?
Or perhaps you follow both of them
for all the joy they bring?

There is merriment and happiness
and festive things to do.
So to all, a Soulful Holiday,
with love from me to you.

21

THE 7 PRINCIPLES OF KWANZAA

UMOJA (UNITY)

KUJICHAGULIA (SELF-DETERMINATION)

UJIMA (COLLECTIVE WORK, RESPONSIBILITY)

UJAMAA (COOPERATIVE ECONOMICS)

NIA (PURPOSE)

KUUMBA (CREATIVITY)

IMANI (FAITH)

Faith over fear.

Future Leader

SUPPORT LOCAL BUSINESS!

Thank you for reading Soulful Holidays. I hope you enjoyed it! As an independent author that writes stories focused on positively highlighting inclusive representation in children's books, gaining exposure relies mostly on word-of-mouth. So if you have the time and inclination, please consider leaving a review wherever you can.

Free downloadable resources for Soulful Holidays and my other book Shiloh and Dande the Lion, can be found on www.ciaralhillbooks.com.

I love picture mail! Share a photo of your family reading Soulful Holidays for a chance to be featured on my social media pages!

Please email your pictures to ciaralhillbooks@gmail.com.

never quit.

Draw a picture of your family